Phonicability

COLLETTE DRIFTE

YEAR 2

b _ _

w _ _ _ _

q _ _ _ _ _

ston_

n _ _ th

Phonicability

CONTENTS

Published by Hopscotch Educational Publishing Ltd,
29 Waterloo Place, Leamington Spa CV32 5LA 01926 744227

© 2000 Hopscotch Educational Publishing

Written by Collette Drifte
Series design by Blade Communications
Illustrated by Susan Hutchison
Cover illustration by Susan Hutchison
Printed by Clintplan, Southam

ISBN 1-902239-52-0

Introduction

ABOUT THE SERIES

'Throughout Key Stage 1, phonics should be the main focus of the 15-minute word level slot in the Literacy Hour.' This is the directive to be found in *Phonics, Progression in phonics: materials for whole-class teaching* issued by the DfEE in 1999. Such an emphasis being placed on the teaching of phonics illustrates its importance.

Phonicability is a series of books which provides individual worksheets that support and consolidate the teaching of phonics skills as outlined in the *National Literacy Strategy Framework for Teaching*. There is one book for each year of Key Stage 1 (Scottish Primary 1–3): *Reception* (Scottish Primary 1), *Year 1* (Scottish Primary 2) and *Year 2* (Scottish Primary 3).

A unique feature of the series is the provision of differentiated photocopiable activity sheets aimed at considerably reducing teacher-preparation time. These sheets present the same activity at three different levels, for below average, average and above average children. They are also differentiated across the year of work, thereby reflecting the expected progress of the child. The worksheets tie in closely with the term-by-term teaching of phonics as detailed in the *National Literacy Framework*. While they leave the teacher free to approach phonics lessons in the most appropriate way for each particular class, they provide a useful extra source of practice material to reinforce and consolidate the teaching points. It is vital that an adult reads the sheets with the children first before expecting them to start work.

Children as young as those at Key Stage 1, who are learning formal literacy and phonics rules for the first time, need a great deal of repetition, practice and consolidation. The provision of as much varied material as possible is essential. Teachers can never have too many ideas and materials for this purpose!

The contents of the books for Reception (Primary 1) and Year 1 (Primary 2) follow a similar format; this is useful for classes with mixed ages.

At the back of each book is a Record/Assessment Sheet. This details the goals for each year, as outlined in the *National Literacy Framework*, and provides a useful record of what the child has achieved, what they need to consolidate and what their next targets should be.

ABOUT THIS BOOK

This book is for teachers of Year 2 children (Primary 1). It aims to:

○ provide differentiated material which will support and consolidate the phonics rules taught during the Literacy Hour
○ provide extension activities that can be worked on independently both during the Literacy Hour and at other (unstructured) times in the day
○ provide repetition and practice of the current rule being taught, while simultaneously reinforcing other aspects of work at word level in the *National Literacy Framework*
○ enable the children to work independently, thus allowing the teacher to work with other groups or individual children simultaneously.

THE PHOTOCOPIABLE ACTIVITY SHEETS

The differentiated sheets introduce the same phonics rule and have the same task, but at three different ability levels. They also provide a variety of activities to consolidate the same teaching point. They are designed to stimulate the children's thinking and to keep up their interest level. The format is not identical on every sheet and so the child will not suffer from 'worksheet fatigue'; boredom is guaranteed to kill motivation!

The activities on each sheet introduce the phonics rule being taught, but they also introduce and use the vocabulary of the *National Literacy Framework*, such as 'vowel', 'consonant', 'digraph' and 'blend'. While these are not among the high frequency words to be taught at Year 2, nevertheless they are words that the children need to become accustomed to hearing and using appropriately. There is also a bonus in seeing them in written form.

Some of the sheets have activities based on 'Look, Say, Cover, Write, Check'. While this is not introduced in the *National Literacy Framework* until Year 3, it is useful for the children to be exposed to the technique gradually and easily. It does not appear on the sheets until Term 2's work; therefore its introduction is not too premature. It is suggested that the teacher models the technique initially, until the children are confident in using it themselves. The activity is self-contained within the sheet, so no additional resources are necessary.

Some of the sheets ask the children to make a wordsearch of their own. These are intended to make the children analyse words containing the phonics rule being taught and give practice in playing with words. It is suggested that these wordsearches are shared among the children so that those who have designed the puzzle have a real 'audience' on whom to try it out.

The order of the activity sheets is not a recommendation to teach the sounds in the same order. They have been presented in the book to follow digraph and blend order as outlined in the *National Literacy Framework* documents. It is suggested that the teacher should read *Phonics, Progression in phonics: materials for whole-class teaching* (DfEE, 1999) and follow its suggestions for teaching order and technique. It is also important to be familiar with the recommended pronunciations in the document. Teaching points in the lesson plans are in line with the document's recommendations. For example, the correct technical terms are adopted, such as 'phoneme' (instead of 'sound'), 'digraph', 'cluster' and 'blend'.

THE EXTENSION ACTIVITIES

The sheets also offer extension activities. These can be done on the back of the sheet and should be done independently, thus eliminating the need for adult supervision, although help with reading the instructions will be needed. The extension activities are designed to reinforce the work done on the main sheet and provide extra practice in the rule being taught.

ASSESSMENT

The sheets themselves build up to provide a portfolio of the child's work and progress. This is a useful resource for assessment and recording, particularly if evidence is needed at a later stage of the child's development. It is suggested that the sheets are kept in a folder or binder. A busy classroom teacher can easily lose sight of how a child performed at the beginning of the year. The sheets will provide evidence of the child's development.

THE ALIEN CHARACTER

Throughout the book (and indeed the series), a space character is used to introduce each phonics rule and to assist the children with the individual activities on the worksheet. The alien in this book is Sherft, whose name comprises an initial consonant digraph, a medial vowel phoneme (phonics rules which are taught during this year) and a final consonant blend.

Some children may not be able to read all of the words on the activity sheets. Therefore, when a classroom session reaches the point of using the sheets, introduce Sherft to them and read the instructions on each sheet with them.

CHAPTER CONTENT

Overall aims
This outlines the aims for the section content.

Teacher's notes
This provides information and suggestions regarding the content of the section.

Intended learning
This states the specific learning goals for the activities.

Suggested activities
This offers suggestions for activities which enable the children to practise, consolidate and reinforce the phoneme being taught. The activities are there for the teacher to pick and choose from according to the class/group needs. They are suggestions only, and as such can be adapted and altered in any way to suit the specific needs of each situation. They are varied in their nature, involving both physical and intellectual abilities.

Using the differentiated activity sheets
This explains the required tasks on the differentiated sheets. It also explains which children will benefit from a specific differentiated sheet.

Plenary session
This suggests ideas for a whole-class discussion of the learning outcome and follow-up work.

Generic sheets
This provides suggestions for further activities with specific generic sheets to be found at the back of the book.

Phonicability

SECTION 1

Revision –
long vowels and
vowel phonemes

Revision – long vowels and vowel phonemes

OVERALL AIMS

❍ To revise the terms 'phoneme', 'vowel', 'consonant', 'blend', 'digraph' and 'cluster'.
❍ To revise the long vowels learned during Year 1.
❍ To sound, recognise and name vowel phonemes 'oo' (short), 'ar', 'oy'/'oi' and 'ow'/'ou'.

TEACHER'S NOTES

Children enjoy using technical terms and need to familiarise themselves with those that are referred to in the *National Literacy Framework*. It is important that they become confident in using these terms correctly and in an appropriate context. While these terms will have been taught and used throughout the Reception (P1) and Year 1 (P2) years, it is important to revise and consolidate them.

A 'phoneme' is the smallest unit of sound in a word. For example, the word 'man' has three phonemes, 'm', 'a' and 'n'. It is vital that children learn to listen to and sound the phonemes represented by the letters of the alphabet.

A 'digraph' is a combination of two letters that produce a single phoneme. For example, 'sh', 'th' and 'ch' are consonant digraphs, while 'ee', 'ai' and 'oa' are vowel digraphs.

A 'blend' is a combination of two letters that produce two phonemes. For example, 'st', 'lp' and 'nd' are consonant blends.

A cluster is a combination of three letters that produce the same number of phonemes. Examples of clusters are 'str', 'thr' and 'ldr' (as in 'ch–il–dren').

LESSON ONE

Intended learning

❍ To revise the terms 'phoneme', 'vowel', 'consonant', 'blend', 'digraph' and 'cluster'.
❍ To listen to, name and sound the long vowels 'ee', 'ai', 'ie', 'oa', 'oo', 'a-e', 'i-e', 'o-e' and 'u-e'.
❍ To name an object or a word that contains these vowels.
❍ To sound, recognise and name vowel phonemes 'oo' (short), 'ar', 'oy'/'oi' and 'ow'/'ou'.
❍ To name an object or a word that contains these vowels.

Starting point: whole class

Write the terms on the board and remind the children that these are words they learned last year. Ask them what the words say. Ask what they mean. If necessary, teach again what each term means.

Write on the board the long vowel(s) being revised. Ask the children whether they can remember the phonemes made by each vowel. Play a game of 'True or False' in which you write a vowel digraph on the board and say "The phoneme for this digraph is …", which could be true or false. The children have to say whether the statement is true or false.

Write on the board the vowel phoneme to be taught in the lesson. Play a game of 'Phoneme football'. Divide the class into two teams named after favourite football clubs (their choice). Each child who can name a word/object containing the appropriate vowel phoneme scores a 'goal' for their team.

Group activities

❍ Using Generic sheet 1, ask the children to write in the phoneme box all the words they can think of containing the revised/new vowel phoneme(s).
❍ Ask the children to draw or paste a picture (from a magazine) of something with the phoneme in it.
❍ Provide a box of mixed plastic alphabet letters and ask the children to sort out the vowel phonemes and use them as templates for a 'vowel phoneme frieze'.
❍ Ask the children to cut out from an enlarged copy of one page of a magazine or newspaper all the words containing the vowel phoneme(s). Stick them on a large sheet of paper. Ask the children to use these words in their writing during the week.
❍ Ask the children to use dictionaries to find words with the vowel phoneme. How many can they list? Ask them to use these words in their writing during the week.

PLENARY SESSION

Each group should report back on what they did. Ensure that, across the term, every child has an opportunity to be their group's 'spokesperson' if they wish to. Ask the children again what each term means.

Ask them to say aloud the revised/new vowel phoneme. Ask, "What have you learned today?", "What did you find easy today?" and "What did you find difficult today?"

LESSON TWO

Intended learning:

❍ To practise saying the name and sound of the revised long vowel phonemes/new vowel phonemes.
❍ To spell and write words containing the phonemes.

Starting point: whole class

Write the vowel phoneme(s) on the board. Ask, "What phoneme is this?", "What is a phoneme?", "What is a digraph?" and "What is a vowel?" Ask for some words that contain the phoneme.

Write some other words on the board, but with the vowel phoneme missing. Ask for volunteers to complete the words. (It is important not to force diffident children to do this.)

Play 'Grandma went to market' but 'buying' items that contain the phoneme.

Play 'Phoneme ping pong'. Child A names another child and says the two vowels in the digraph, Child B says the phoneme then names another child and two new vowels. For example, David says, "Ellen, 'a' and 'i'"; Ellen says, "'ai'; Pritpal, 'i' and 'e'"; Pritpal says "'ie'; Anne, 'o' and 'o'." Set speed records and play on a daily basis.

Introduce the activity sheets. Show the picture of Sherft to the children and explain that Sherft's name is made up of some of the phonemes they will be learning, ie initial consonant digraph, medial long vowel digraph and final consonant blend. Read the instructions on each sheet to the groups.

USING THE DIFFERENTIATED ACTIVITY SHEETS

Activity sheets a

These are for children whose output may be limited in the time available. They give the opportunity to analyse words, sound out the phoneme and do a small amount of independent writing.

Activity sheets b

These are for children who are able to do a little more work within a limited time period. The writing content is more demanding.

Activity sheets c

These are for children who are able to recall the phonemes with confidence. They will be able to do more writing within the time given and to do it independently.

PLENARY SESSION

Choose a child from each group to explain what their group did on their sheets. Make a display of some of the sheets while the revision work is still being done.

Ask, "What have you learned from today's lesson?", "Was there anything you didn't understand about today's lesson?", "What were the phonemes we revised/learned today?" and "What were the terms we revised today?"

GENERIC SHEETS

❍ Generic sheet 1 has blank phoneme boxes. These can be used to find new words with the required phoneme in them. The sheet can be used either as the basis of a search game or as a reference bank of words containing that specific phoneme.
❍ Generic sheet 2 has blank grids that can be used to design wordsearches or crosswords. Several of the activity sheets give this as a task and this generic sheet can be used as the photocopiable master. The grids differ in size for different ability children.
❍ Generic sheet 3 has the blank outline of a cube which can be copied on to card, cut out and used as a dice in phoneme games.
❍ Generic sheet 4 has blanks which can be used for Pelmanism, dominoes or Snap, as required. The appropriate phoneme can be written on each card.

8

Do you remember these phonemes? *ee* and *ea*.

Sherft

◆Join the words to the pictures.

sleep

meat

sheep

seat

◆Read the words aloud.

◆Write *ee* or *ea* to finish the words.

tr __ __

f __ __ t

gr __ __ n

l __ __ f

__ __ t

b __ __ ns

◆Read the words aloud.

Write sentences for three of the words.

Do you remember these phonemes? *ee* and *ea*.

Sherft

◆ Finish the words and join them to the pictures.

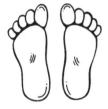

f _ _ t

tr _ _

thr _ _

3   sw _ _ t

toffee

s _ _ l

l _ _ f

p _ _ s

st _ _ m

◆ Read the words aloud.

◆ Find a rhyme for

Write sentences for each of these words.

feet

seal

tree

steam

10

Sherft

Do you remember these phonemes? *ee* and *ea*.

◆ Write the words and join them to the pictures.

Beans

b _ _ _ _ _

l _ _ _ _

t _ _ _

_ _ _

_ _ _ _

b _ _ _

w _ _ _ _ _

q _ _ _ _ _

_ _ _ _ _

_ _ _ _ _

◆ Read the words aloud.

◆ Find rhymes for these words.

bee team sleep

peas wheel eat

Write sentences for these words.

Do you remember these phonemes? *ai* and *ay*.

Sherft

◆ Do the wordsearch. You may go across or down. Sometimes a letter is used twice.

a	n	t	a	p
m	a	i	l	a
e	i	d	a	y
p	l	c	a	p

mail

pay

nail

day

◆ Read the words aloud.

◆ Write *ai* or *ay* to finish the words.

tr _ _

s _ _

◆ Find words to rhyme with these. Say them aloud.

Write your rhyming words.

erft

Do you remember these phonemes? *ai* and *ay*.

Sherft

◆ Do the wordsearch. You may go across or down. Sometimes a letter is used twice.

m	a	s	a	i	l
c	h	a	i	n	a
l	a	y	w	e	n
a	t	m	a	t	i
p	i	t	y	a	i
t	r	a	i	n	n

train

say

chain

lay

sail

way

◆ Read the words aloud.

◆ Write *ai* or *ay* to finish the words.

m _ _ l

d _ _

s _ _

sn _ _ l

◆ Find words to rhyme with these. Say them aloud.

Write your rhyming words.

12

Sherft

Do you remember these phonemes? *ai* and *ay*.

◆ Do the wordsearch. You may go across or down. Sometimes a letter is used twice.

w	m	a	i	l	t	a
a	i	p	p	a	a	i
y	t	l	a	i	i	l
d	r	a	i	n	l	p
s	a	y	l	a	i	l
a	y	f	l	a	m	i

way
pail
tray
tail
say
drain
play
mail

◆ Read the words aloud.

◆ Write the correct phoneme to finish each word.

ch _ _ n

st _ _

tr _ _

tr _ _ l

w _ _

st _ _ n

◆ Find words to rhyme with these. Say them aloud.

Write your rhyming words.

Do you remember these phonemes? *ie igh y*

Sherft

◆ Read these words aloud.

tried

high

fly

◆ Now try these.

dried

flight

dry

◆ Can you find a new word for the phoneme boxes?

ie	

igh	

y	

Look at your friend's new words. Read them aloud.

14

Do you remember these phonemes? *ie igh y*

◆ Read these words aloud.

cried   tried

flight   high

dry   try

◆ Now try these.

dried

night

sky

◆ Can you find some new words for the phoneme boxes?

| ie | 1. |
| | 2. |

| igh | 1. |
| | 2. |

| y | 1. |
| | 2. |

Look at your friend's new words. Read them aloud.

Do you remember these phonemes? *ie igh y*

Sherft

◆ Read these words aloud.

fried   tried   cried

night   high   fright

dry   sky   try

◆ Now try these.

dried

flight

fry

◆ Can you find some new words for the phoneme boxes?

ie	1.
	2.
	3.

igh	1.
	2.
	3.

y	1.
	2.
	3.

Sherft

Look at your friend's new words. Read them aloud.

Do you remember these phonemes? *oa* *ow*

Sherft

◆Match the picture to the word.

blow

coat   *bow*

loaf   *goat*

snow

◆Write the words in the correct phoneme box.

oa

ow

Write a sentence for one word from each phoneme box.

18

Do you remember these phonemes? *oa*   *ow*

Sherft

◆ Match the picture to the word.

road

arrow

bowl

bow   goal

goat

loaf   mow

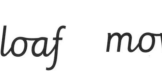

◆ Write the words in the correct phoneme box.

oa	

ow	

Look in a dictionary for words you don't know.

Write a sentence for one word from each phoneme box.

Do you remember these phonemes? *oa   ow*

Sherft

◆Match the picture to the word.

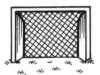

foam   *throw*

coach   *snow*

toad

goal

blow   *pillow*

moat

arrow

◆Write the words into the correct phoneme box.

oa	

ow	

Look in a dictionary for words you don't know. Write sentences for two words from each phoneme box.

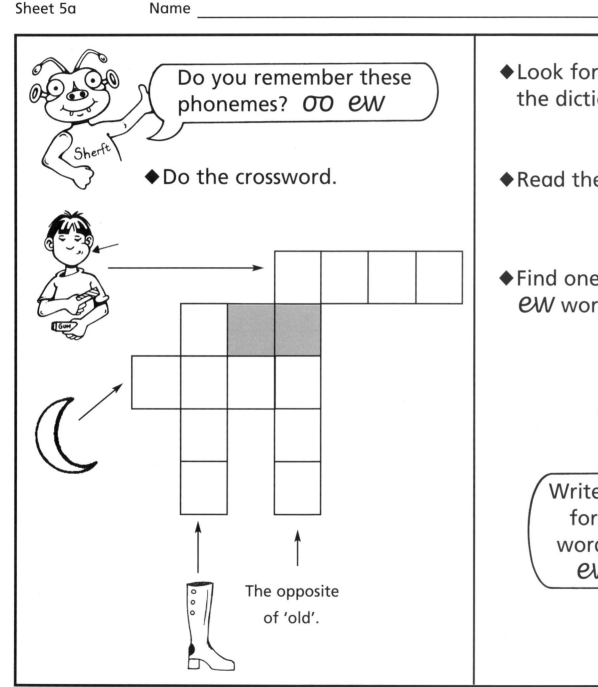

Do you remember these phonemes? *oo* *ew*

Sherft

◆ Do the crossword.

The opposite of 'old'.

◆ Look for your *oo* and *ew* words in the dictionary.

◆ Read the words aloud.

◆ Find one new *oo* word and one new *ew* word.

Write sentences for one *oo* word and one *ew* word.

Sherft

Do you remember these phonemes? *oo ew*

◆ Do the crossword.

What we eat.

The bird ___ away.

◆ Read the words aloud.

◆ Look for the words in a dictionary.

◆ Find two new *oo* words and two new *ew* words.

Write sentences for two *oo* words and two *ew* words.

Do you remember these phonemes? oo ew

◆ Do the crossword.

When you cook meat and vegetables all together.

Not many is only a ____ .

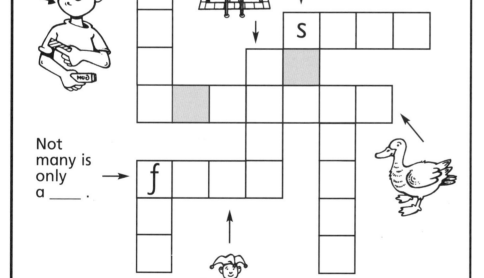

◆ Look for the words in a dictionary.

◆ Read the words aloud.

◆ Find three new oo words and three new ew words.

Write sentences for three oo words and three ew words.

Sherft ©

23

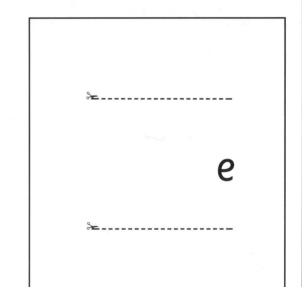

What happens to *a* when you put *e* at the end of a word?

Sherft

tap + e ⟶ _____

man + e ⟶ _____

cap + e ⟶ _____

◆ Read the words aloud.

◆ Make this word slide.
  Write the words and read them aloud.

can

mat

pan

e

Write some sentences for your words.

24

What happens to **a** when you put **e** at the end of a word?

Sherft

mat + e ⟶ _____

can + e ⟶ _____

hat + e ⟶ _____

tap + e ⟶ _____

◆Read the words aloud.

◆Make this word slide.
Write the words and read them aloud.

lan

gam

pan

bak

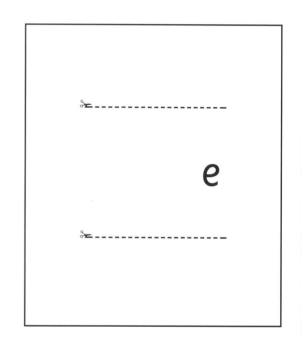

e

Write some sentences for your words.

What happens to *a* when you put *e* at the end of a word?

Sherft

man + e ——→ _____

hat + e ——→ _____

cap + e ——→ _____

tap + e ——→ _____

can + e ——→ _____

◆ Read the words aloud.

◆ Make this word slide.
  Write the words and read them aloud.

cak

flam

tak

cran

blam

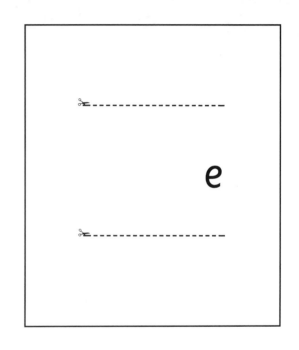

e

Write some sentences for your words.

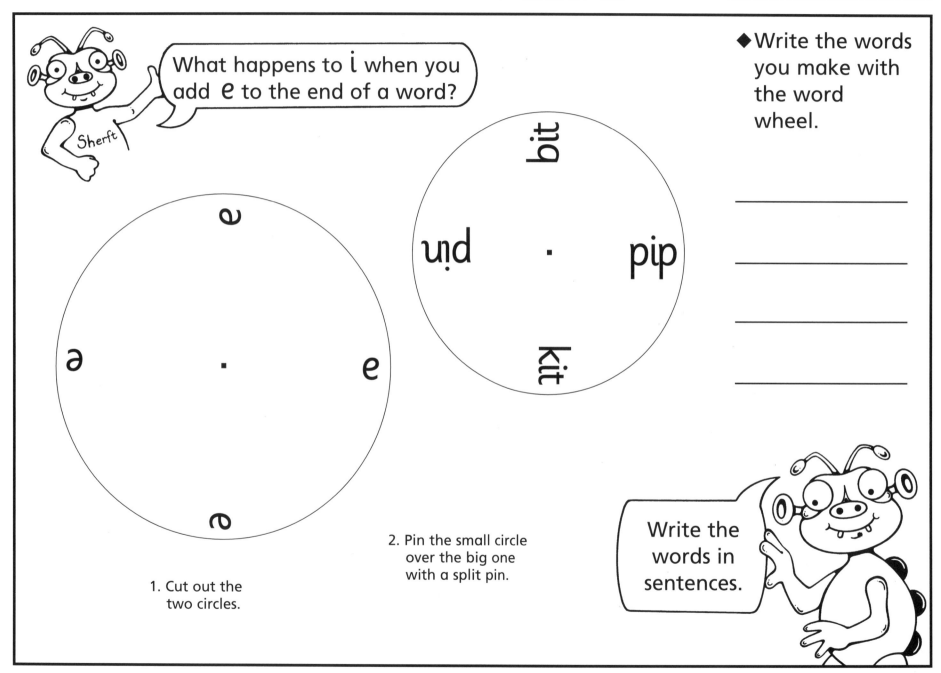

What happens to i when you add e to the end of a word?

Sherft

◆Write the words you make with the word wheel.

_____

_____

_____

_____

1. Cut out the two circles.

2. Pin the small circle over the big one with a split pin.

Write the words in sentences.

Name _____   Date _____

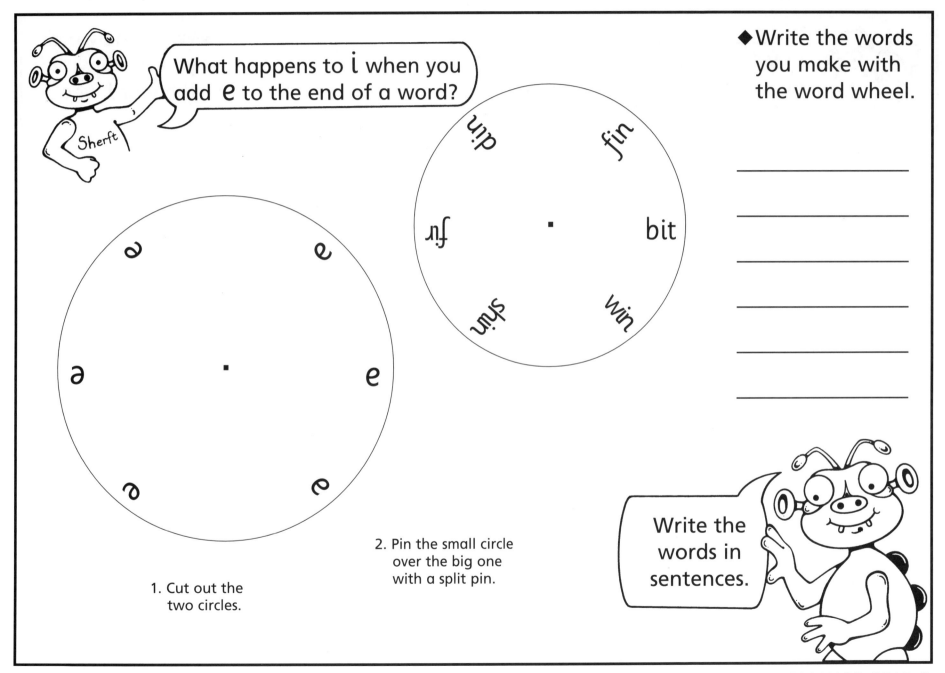

What happens to **i** when you add **e** to the end of a word?

◆ Write the words you make with the word wheel.

1. Cut out the two circles.

2. Pin the small circle over the big one with a split pin.

Write the words in sentences.

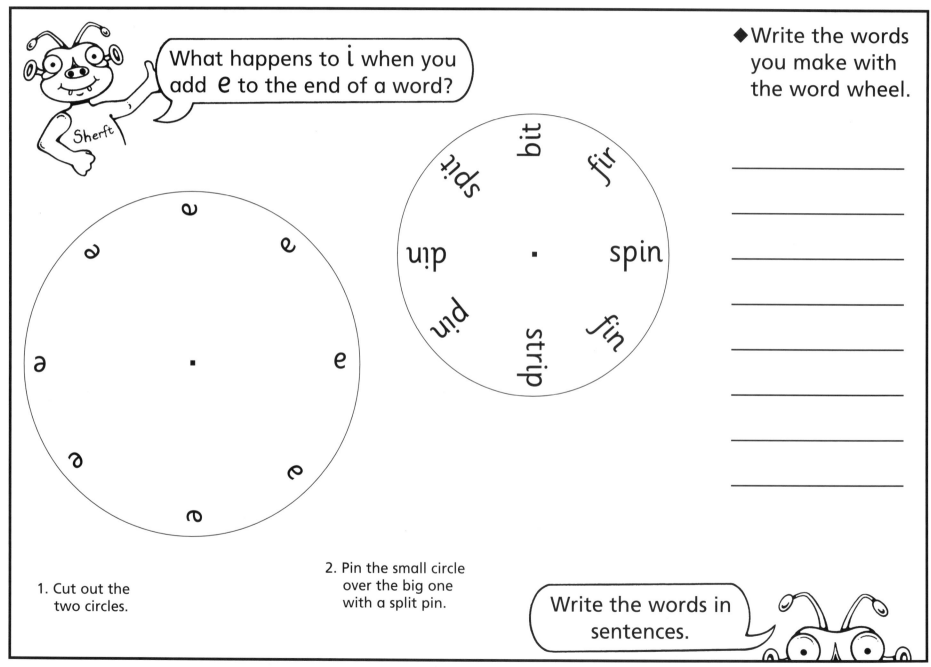

What happens to **i** when you add **e** to the end of a word?

Sherft

◆ Write the words you make with the word wheel.

_____

_____

_____

_____

_____

_____

_____

_____

1. Cut out the two circles.

2. Pin the small circle over the big one with a split pin.

Write the words in sentences.

What happens to **o** when you add **e** to the end of these?

Sherft

ros_   hol_   bon_   e

◆ Add **e** to finish the words. Read them aloud.

_____   _____   _____

◆ Find two more **o − e** words.

Now write your new words in sentences.

_____

_____

30

◆ Add e to finish the words. Read them aloud.

_____   _____   _____   _____

◆ Find three more o—e words.

_____   _____

_____

Now write your new words in sentences.

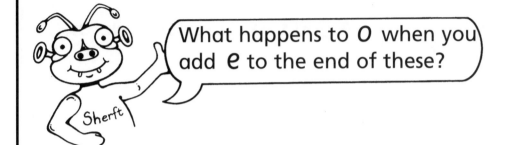

What happens to **o** when you add **e** to the end of these?

smok_   not_   ston_   glob_   strok_   e

◆ Add **e** to finish the words. Read them aloud.

_____   _____   _____   _____   _____

◆ Find four more **o_e** words.

Now write your new words in sentences.

_____   _____

_____   _____

What happens to u when you add e to the end of a word?

Sherft

Find two more u_e words.

Look them up in a dictionary.

Write them.

_____

_____

Put the missing letters into the words.

Write the words again. Read them aloud.

Write your new u_e words in sentences.

_____   _____   _____

32

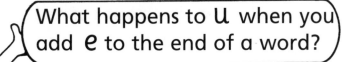

What happens to u when you add e to the end of a word?

Sherft

◆ Find three more u_e words.

◆ Look them up in a dictionary.

◆ Write them.

_____

_____

_____

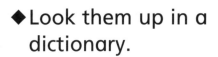

◆ Put the missing letters into the words.

◆ Write the words again. Read them aloud.

_____ _____

_____ _____

Write your new u_e words in sentences.

34

What happens to **u** when you add **e** to the end of a word?

◆ Find four more **u_e** words.

◆ Look them up in a dictionary.

◆ Write them.

_____

_____

_____

_____

◆ Put the missing letters into the words.

◆ Write the words again. Read them aloud.

_____ _____ _____

_____ _____

Write your new **u_e** words in sentences.

This time _oo_ has a different phoneme.

◆ Join the word to the picture.

book

foot   wool

cook

◆ Read the words aloud. What phoneme does _oo_ make?

◆ Use the letters on the sails to make _oo_ words.

◆ Write the words.

_____

_____

_____

Find two more _oo_ words. Write them.

36

This time oo has a different phoneme.

Sherft

◆Join the word to the picture.

crook

hook

wood

foot

◆Read the words aloud. What phoneme does oo make?

◆Use the letters on the sails to make oo words.

◆Write the words.

_____   _____

_____   _____

Find three more oo words. Write them.

This time **oo** has a different phoneme.

Sherft

◆ Finish the words and join them to the pictures.

w _ _ _

h _ _ _

sh _ _ k

c _ _ _

b _ _ _

◆ Read the words aloud. What phoneme does **oo** make?

◆ Use the letters on the sails to make **oo** words.

br _ k   oo

cr _ k   oo

st _ d   oo

h _ d   oo

t _ k   oo

◆ Write the words.

_____   _____

_____   _____

_____

Find four more **oo** words. Write them.

Sherft

37

Write **ar** to finish the words.

Sherft

j _ _   st _ _   c _ _

◆Read the words aloud.

◆Now finish these **ar** words.

d _ _ t   f _ _ m

h _ _ d

◆Make some **ar** words from the letters in the wheel.

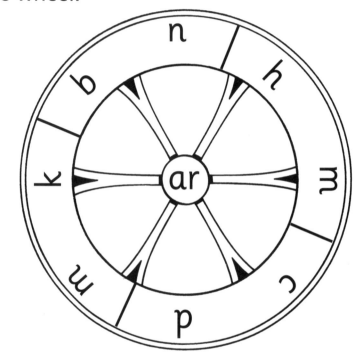

_____

_____

_____

_____

Now write your words in sentences.

Write **ar** to finish the words.

Sherft

c _ _ ds   h _ _ p   sc _ _ f

◆ Read the words aloud.

◆ Now finish these **ar** words.

b _ _ n   st _ _

j _ _   f _ _ m

◆ Make some **ar** words from the letters in the wheel.

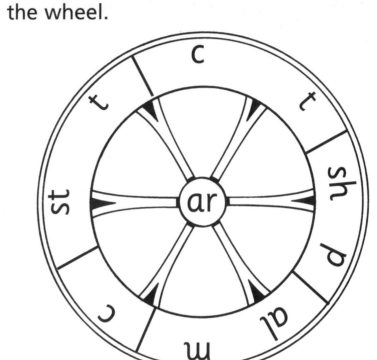

_____

_____

_____

_____

Now write your words in sentences.

Write **ar** to finish the words.

_ _ _ _ _

g _ _ _ _ _

_ _ _ _ s t

_ _ _ _

◆Read the words aloud.

◆ Make some **ar** words from the letters in the wheel.

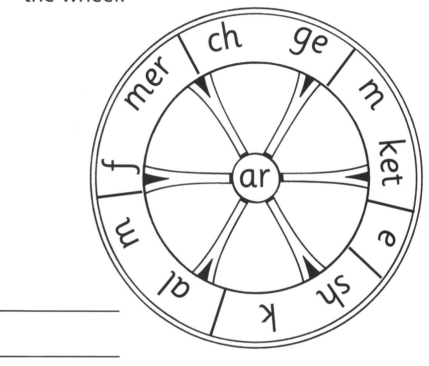

_____

_____

_____

_____

_____

_____

◆Read the words aloud.

Now write your words in sentences.

oy
Draw a circle around each
oy you can see.

oy   ay   oy   ay

ay   oy   ay

ey   ay   ey

oy   oy   oy

ay   oy   ay

◆How many did you find?

◆Do the crossword.

◆Write the words
and read them
aloud.

_____

_____

Look in a
dictionary for
'enjoy' and
'joy'.

42

oy
Draw a circle around each **oy** you can see.

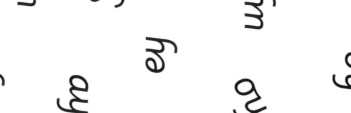

◆How many did you find? ☐

◆Do the crossword.

A word that means you like doing something.

A word that means happiness.

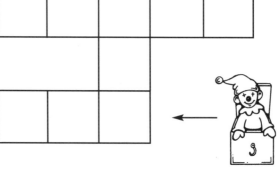

◆Write the words and read them aloud.

_____

_____

_____

_____

Look in a dictionary for 'oyster' and 'destroy'.

oy
Draw a circle around each **oy** you can see.

Sherft

uy   ho   ay   ho

oy   ey

oy   oy   ey   uy

ho   uy   oy   ey

ey

ey   ey   oy   uy   oy

◆How many did you find? ☐

◆Do the crossword.

You play with it. ↓

When someone breaks something to pieces. ←

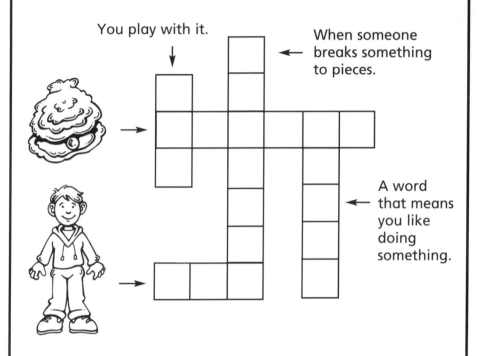

A word that means you like doing something. ←

◆Write the words and read them aloud.

_____ _____ _

_____ _ _____

Look in a dictionary for 'employ' and 'loyal'.

43

44

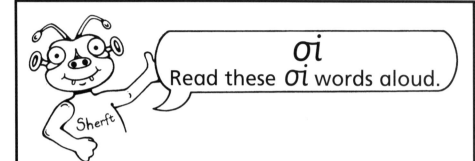

oi
Read these oi words aloud.

Sherft

boil

coins

soil

◆Look for the words in a dictionary.

◆Write a sentence for one of the words.

_____

◆Finish the words in the tortoise's shell.

Hello. I'm a boy tortoise!

_ _ l
c _ _ ns   j _ _ n
p _ _ nt   s _ _ l

◆Write the words.

_____   _____

_____   _____

_____

Write a sentence for one of the words.

Sherft

oi
Read these oi words aloud.

join

point

spoil

coins

◆Look for the words in a dictionary.

◆Write sentences for two of the words.

_____

_____

◆Finish the words in the tortoise's shell.

Hello. I'm a boy tortoise!

b _ _ l

c _ _ n

s _ _ l

j _ _ n

_ _ l

p _ _ nt

◆Write the words.

_____   _____

_____   _____

_____   _____

Write sentences for two of the words.

oi

Read these *oi* words aloud.

Sherft

moist

joint

spoil

hoist

point

◆ Look for the words in a dictionary.

◆ Write a sentence for three of the words.

_____

_____

_____

◆ Finish the words in the tortoise's shell.

Hello. I'm a boy tortoise!

sp _ _ _ l

s _ _ _ l   _ _ _ l   j _ _ n

tort _ _ _ se   m _ _ _ st

◆ Write the words.

_____   _____

_____   _____

_____   _____

Write sentences for three of the words.

_ou_

Read these words aloud.

Sherft

loud   our   flour   out

◆ Write _ou_ to finish the words.

h _ _ se   f _ _ nd   sh _ _ t

◆ Read the words aloud.

◆ Can you find some new words for the _ou_ phoneme box?

_ou_
1.
2.
3.

◆ Write a sentence for one of your words.

_____

Read your friend's new words aloud.

48

ou

Read these words aloud.

flour house aloud about our hour

◆ Finish the words.

m _ _ se   s _ _ nd   _ _ t

l _ _ d   c _ _ nt

◆ Read the words aloud.

◆ Can you find some new words for the *ou* phoneme box?

ou
1.
2.
3.
4.

◆ Write a sentence for two of your words.

_____

_____

Read your friend's new words aloud.

ou
Read these words aloud.

ground mouse loud shout about

our sound house

◆Finish the words.

al _ _ d   c _ _ nt   fl _ _ r

f _ _ nd   _ _ t   d _ _ bt

◆Read the words aloud.

◆Can you find some new words for the **ou** phoneme box?

ou
1.
2.
3.
4.
5.

◆Write a sentence for three of your words.

_____

_____

_____

Read your friend's new words aloud.

ow

Put a circle around the correct word.

crowd   crown

flower   frown

cow   cowboy

◆ Do the *OW* wordsearch. You may go across or down. Sometimes a letter is used twice.

c	o	w	b	l
o	d	w	r	o
n	o	w	o	n
o	w	l	w	w
u	n	o	n	o

brown

cow

owl

down

now

◆ Read the words aloud.

Make a wordsearch with five new *ow* words.

ow
Put a circle around the correct word.

crowd   crown

frown   flower

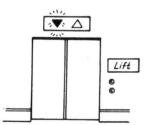

down   brown

◆ Do the **ow** wordsearch. You may go across or down. Sometimes a letter is used twice.

n	a	d	o	w	g
f	l	o	w	e	r
r	l	w	e	r	o
o	o	n	o	w	w
w	w	o	o	e	l
n	c	r	o	w	n

flower
down
growl
crown
allow
now
frown

◆ Read the words aloud.

Make a wordsearch with seven new **ow** words.

ow
Put a circle around the correct word.

growl   glower

shower   flower

crown   clown

◆ Do the **ow** wordsearch. You may go across or down. Sometimes a letter is used twice.

f	l	d	o	w	e	s
s	h	o	w	e	r	f
c	o	w	f	r	g	l
r	f	n	o	w	r	o
o	l	a	l	l	o	w
w	c	o	b	o	w	e
d	o	w	o	e	l	r

bow
growl
allow
flower
crowd
cow
down
shower
now

◆ Read the words aloud.

Make a wordsearch with nine new **ow** words.

Phonicability

SECTION 2

Vowel/consonant digraphs, consonant digraphs and compound words

Vowel/consonant digraphs, consonant digraphs and compound words

OVERALL AIMS

○ To sound, recognise and name the digraphs 'air', 'are', 'ere', 'ear', 'or', 'oor', 'aw', 'au', 'ore', 'er', 'ir' and 'ur'.
○ To name and write words that include these digraphs.
○ To sound, recognise and name the consonant digraphs 'ch' (hard), 'ph' and 'wh'.
○ To name and write words that include these consonant digraphs.
○ To be able to recognise, split and form compound words, both verbally and in written form.

TEACHER'S NOTES

The digraphs taught in this chapter are more complicated than those learned during the Reception year and Year 1. Some of them have identical spellings to earlier words, but have different phonemes. For example, 'are' is now sounded as in 'scare'; 'ear' as in 'bear'. It is important to bring these differences to the attention of the children.

It is also important that, in the same way they learn to split words into phonemes, the children learn to split compound words into the smaller word components. To develop the ability to analyse a word at all levels is essential for good reading and writing skills. Young children derive immense pleasure from finding words 'hidden' within others and are usually amazed at the number of compound words they actually know once they start to think of them.

LESSON ONE

Intended learning:

○ To sound, recognise and name the vowel digraph or consonant digraph being taught.
○ To name a word or object that contains the vowel or consonant digraph being taught.
○ To analyse a compound word and split it into its smaller word components.

Starting point: whole class

Write the digraph being taught on the board and tell the children what phoneme it makes. Ask them to tell you the correct term for two letters making a single phoneme. If necessary, remind them that it is 'digraph'.

Ask several children to write the phoneme on the board, saying it out loud simultaneously.

Write one or two words on the board that contain the phoneme being taught. Explain that it is called a 'vowel/consonant digraph'. Ask for some other words which include that phoneme. Give assistance if needed.

Write up some examples of compound words. Tell the children that they're going to look for the hidden words within the main word. Ask for volunteers to write the smaller words on the board.

On another occasion, write the smaller words on the board. Ask for volunteers to join together the words to make compound words.

Write up a mixture of true compound words and non-compound words (football, uncomfortable, somewhere, display). Ask "Which are true compound words?" (Words that can be split up into 'real' words.

Group activities

○ Using Generic sheet 2, ask the children to make a wordsearch with words which include the digraph.
○ Ask the children to draw or paste a picture (from a magazine) of something with the digraph in it. Ask them to write a sentence using the word.
○ Ask the children to look in a dictionary for words with the digraph. Make the words with plastic letters in a tray. Keep the tray as a display while the phoneme is being taught.
○ Ask the children to find all the compound words on an enlarged copy of a magazine page and mark them with a highlighting pen.
○ Make a three-column chart for compound words: two columns to contain the smaller words and one for the compound word. Use different colours for the different components.

Plenary session

Each group should report back on what they did. Use the tray of plastic letters/words to discuss the phoneme. With the whole class, read the compound words chart the children have produced. Does everyone agree? Can anyne think of other example?

Ask the children, "What word have you learned today?", "What is a compound word?", "What did you find difficult today?" and "What did you find easy?"

LESSON TWO

Intended learning:

○ To recognise, name and sound the digraph being taught.
○ To practise writing the letters representing the digraph.
○ To practise using the digraph in its appropriate position in a word.
○ To practise splitting and rejoining compound words.

Starting point: whole class

Write the previous lesson's digraph on the board. Ask "What phoneme does this digraph make?", "What is a digraph?" and "What words have this digraph in them?" Ask for three or four volunteers to write words on the board.

Display the compound words chart made by the children. Discuss the words on it. Ask "What is a compound word?" and "What is important about the smaller words inside it?" If necessary, remind the children that the smaller words have to be words in their own right.

Introduce the activity sheets. Read the instructions on each sheet to the groups.

THE DIFFERENTIATED ACTIVITY SHEETS

Before distributing the activity sheets, read the instructions on each sheet with the groups. In this term's activity sheets, the technique of 'Look, Say, Cover, Write, Check' is introduced. This needs to be explained to and modelled for the children to ensure that they understand how it works and why it is done. Since this is a strategy that they will be employing throughout the rest of their Primary School careers, it is vital that they are well grounded in using the method.

Activity sheets a

These are for children who need repetition of the digraph being taught. They encourage them to look carefully at the formation of the digraph both as an entity and in its position in a word. Compound words are introduced with simple activities.

Activity sheets b

These are for children who are able to do a little independent writing. They encourage them to look carefully at the formation of the digraph and to place it in its position in a word. Compound words are introduced with more demanding activities than those in Activity sheet a.

Activity sheets c

These are for children who can confidently write a few words independently. They encourage them to look carefully at the formation of the digraph and to place it in its position in a word. Compound words are introduced with challenging activities.

All levels have some sheets which include cloze procedure activities, wordsearches or wordplay.

PLENARY SESSION

Choose a child from each group to explain what their group did on their sheets. Ensure that across the term, every child has an opportunity to be their group's 'spokesperson'. Make a display of some of the sheets while that digraph is still being taught and consolidated.

Ask "What have you learned from today's lesson?", "Was there anything you didn't understand about today's lesson?", "What was the digraph we learned today?' and "What phoneme does it make?"

Ask the children to think of some words which contain the digraph.

Ask "How many compound words can we think of in two minutes?" Ask for volunteers to write the words on the board.

56

air
Finish these sentences.

shoes

This is a p _ _ _ of shoes.

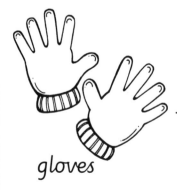

gloves

This is _____
_____

◆ Draw another pair.

◆ Write the sentence.

This is _____

◆ Read these words.

hair
fair
chair

Write the words in sentences.

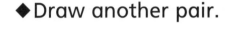

air

Finish these sentences.

◆ Draw another pair.

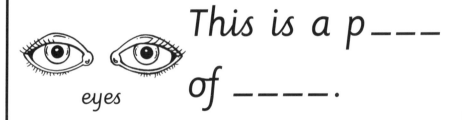

eyes

This is a p___ of ____.

◆ Write the sentence.

_____

boots

This is _____

_____

◆ Read these words.

chair

stairs

fair

Write the words in sentences.

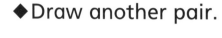

air
Finish these sentences.

This is a p___

of _____.

mittens

This _____

_____

trousers

◆ Draw another pair.

◆ Write the sentence.

_____

◆ Read these words.

stairs

hair

fair

chair

Write the words in sentences.

Name _____ Date _____

-are

Look for these **-are** words in the dictionary.

bare

dare

hare

◆Turn over and write a sentence for each word.

◆Draw a circle around all the **-are** words.

hear

queer

clear

square

stare

cheer

fear

share

hare

near

dare

steer

dear

bare

dare

hare

Name _____   Date _____

-are

Look for these -are words in the dictionary.

share

glare

rare

scare

◆Turn over and write a sentence for each word.

◆Draw a circle around all the -are words.

dear

steer

dare

share

hear

sheer

spare

hare

rare

fear

square

tear

near

bare

Look
say
cover
write
check

Fold

share

glare

rare

scare

60

Look
say
cover
write
check

Fold

61

–are

Look for these **-are**
words in the dictionary.

stare

glare

rare

declare

bare

◆Turn over and
write a sentence
for each word.

◆Draw a circle around all
the **-are** words.

hear

dear

spare

scare

declare

tear

stare

fear

dare

near

queer

share

glare

steer

rare

bare

stare

glare

rare

declare

bare

-ere

-ere sounds like 'ear' when it's here, but

-ere sounds like 'air' when it's there.

Where?

There!

◆ Make the **-ere** words.

some + wh + ere → _____

no + wh + ere → _____

any + wh + ere → _____

Write a sentence for one of the words.

Name _____   Date _____

–ere

–ere sounds like 'ear' when it's here, but

–ere sounds like 'air' when it's there.

Where?

There!

◆ Make the -**ere** words.

wh + ere → _____

any + wh + ere → _____

some + wh + ere → _____

no + wh + ere → _____

Write sentences for two of the words.

ere

-ere sounds like 'ear' when it's here, but
-ere sounds like 'air' when it's there.
Where?
There!

◆Make the **-ere** words.

         th   +   ere ⟶ _____

no   +   wh   +   ere ⟶ _____

any   +   wh   +   ere ⟶ _____

         wh   +   ere ⟶ _____

some   +   wh   +   ere ⟶ _____

Write sentences for three of the words.

ear
Read the poem.

Here's a bear

With tears

In the clothes

That he wears.

◆What does *ear* sound like in these words? Here or there?

◆Make the —*ear* word slide.

b

t

w

_____

ear

_____

Write a sentence for each word.

66

ear
Read the poem.

Here's a bear

With tears

In the clothes

That he wears.

◆ Does *ear* sound like *eer* or *air* in these words?

◆ Make the –*ear* word slide.

p
t
w
b

_ _ _ _ _ _ _ _ _ _ _ _
ear
_ _ _ _ _ _ _ _ _ _ _ _

Write a sentence for each word.

ear
Read the poem.

Here's a bear

With tears

In the clothes

That he wears.

◆What phoneme does *ear* make in the poem? Circle the letters below that have the same phoneme.

are air eer ier

◆Make the -*ear* word slide.

sw

w

p

b

t

✂ - - - - - - - - - - - - - - -

ear

✂ - - - - - - - - - - - - - - -

Write a sentence for each word.

or

Match the **or** words to the pictures.

horns

shorts

fork

corn

◆ Choose the correct word to finish the sentences.

torn horse worn

1. The boy rode the _____ very fast.

2. I have _____ a hole in my jumper.

3. Dad has _____ the same socks for a week!

Find two more **or** words.

or

Write *or* to finish the words. Then join them to the pictures.

h _ _ se

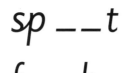

t _ _ n

sp _ _ t

f _ _ k

◆ Choose the correct word to finish the sentences.

sort corn port horns

1. The _ _ _ _ was growing in the field.

2. The ship sailed into _ _ _ _.

3. The cow had long _ _ _ _ _.

4. Can you _ _ _ _ out the words?

Find three more *or* words.

70

or

Finish the words and then join them to the pictures.

n__th

sh__ts

st__m

h__se

p__t

c__n

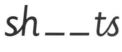

◆ Choose the correct word to finish the sentences.

fork   torn   short   horse   born

1. Mum was _ _ _ _ on 13 February 1975.

2. The baby had _ _ _ _ _ hair.

3. We eat with a knife and a _ _ _ _ .

4. The _ _ _ _ _ galloped around the field.

5. The tramp wore _ _ _ _ trousers.

Find four more
or words.

oor

Sherft

◆Do the *oor* wordsearch. The arrows tell you which way the words go.

◆Sometimes a letter is used twice.

◆Look carefully!

m	p	o	o	r
f	l	d	m	d
f	l	o	o	r
p	r	o	o	m
p	o	r	r	o

poor →

door ↓

floor →

moor ↓

Write two of the words in sentences.

Sherft

72

oor

Sherft

◆ Do the *oor* wordsearch. The arrows tell you which way the words go.

◆ Sometimes a letter is used twice.

◆ Two of the words are used twice. Look carefully!

p	r	d	m	f	d
d	o	o	r	l	m
m	o	d	m	o	r
o	d	p	d	o	o
o	p	o	o	r	o
r	m	p	d	m	p

poor →   and ↑

floor   ↓

moor   ↓

door →   and ↑

Write three of the words in sentences.

Sherft ©

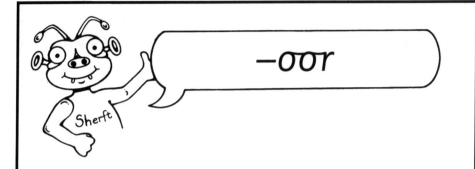

-oor

◆ Do the *oor* wordsearch. The arrows tell you which way the words go.

◆ Sometimes a letter is used twice.

◆ The words are used twice. Look carefully!

poor	↓	and	↑
floor	→	and	←
moor	←	and	↓
door	→	and	↑

r	d	p	r	o	o	m
o	r	o	o	l	f	d
o	o	o	f	d	m	m
p	o	r	p	m	o	f
m	d	o	o	r	o	p
f	l	o	o	r	r	d

Write the words in sentences.

74

ore

Draw a circle around each **ore** that you can see.

are   are   are

ore   ore   are   ere   ore

ere   ore   are

ore   ere   ore

◆How many did you find? ☐

◆Make some **ore** words from the letters in the wheel.

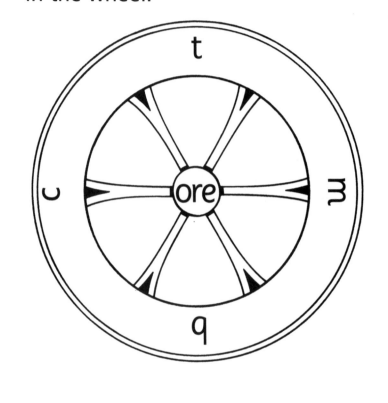

_____

_____

Write your words in sentences.

ore

Draw a circle around each ore that you can see.

◆ Make some ore words from the letters in the wheel.

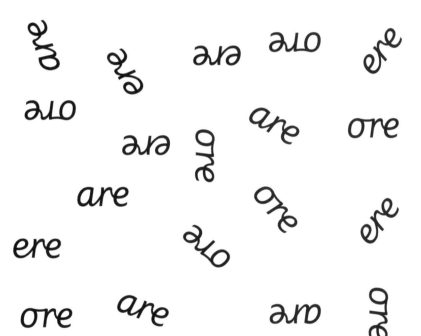

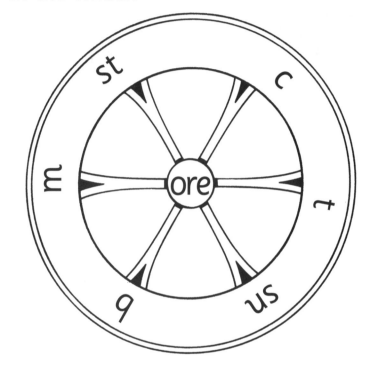

◆How many did you find?

I found _____

_____   _____

_____   _____

_____

Write your words in sentences.

ore

Draw a circle around each **ore** that you can see.

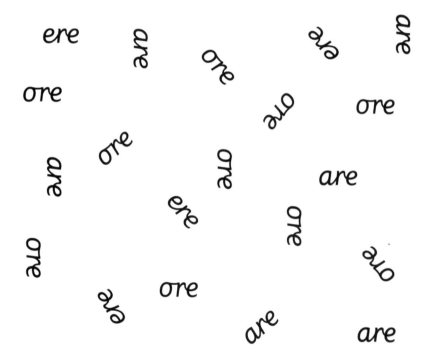

◆ How many did you find?

_____

◆ Make some **ore** words from the letters in the wheel.

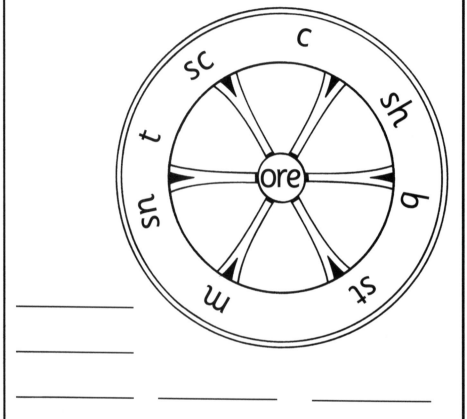

_____ _____

_____ _____

_____ _____ _____

_____ _____ _____

Write your words in sentences.

76

Name _____ Date _____

Look
say
cover
write
check

Fold

au
Look for these au words in the dictionary.

Sherft

haunt
fault
daughter

◆Read the words aloud.

◆Write a sentence for each word.

_____

_____

_____

_____

_____

_____

◆Ask your friend to read your sentences aloud.

haunt fault daughter

Name _____   Date _____

Look
say
cover
write
check

Fold

au
Look for these *au* words in the dictionary.

◆ Write a sentence for each word.

_____

_____

_____

_____

_____

_____

_____

_____

_____

caught

sauna

taut

daughter

◆ Read the words aloud.

◆ Ask your friend to read your sentences aloud.

caught sauna taut daughter

Name _____ Date _____

au
Look for these au words in the dictionary.

◆ Write a sentence for each word.

_____
_____
_____
_____
_____
_____
_____
_____
_____
_____
_____

launch

daub

jaunt

saunter

daughter

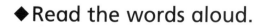

◆ Read the words aloud.

◆ Ask your friend to read your sentences aloud.

Look
say
cover
write
check

Fold

79

launch daub jaunt saunter daughter

aw
Read these words aloud.

Sherft

paw saw jaw dawn

◆Write aw to finish these words.

cl__ dr__ th__

◆Read the words aloud.

◆Look for them in a dictionary.

◆Can you find some new words for the aw phoneme box?

aw
1.
2.
3.

◆Write a sentence for one of your words.

Read your friend's new words aloud.

80

Sherft

aw
Read these words aloud.

claw draw thaw crawl

paw dawn

◆ Finish these words.

pr _ _ n   str _ _   j _ _

dr _ _ er   sp _ _ n

◆ Read the words aloud.

◆ Can you find some new words for the **aw** phoneme box?

aw
1.
2.
3.
4.

◆ Write a sentence for two of your words.

_____

_____

Read your friend's
new words aloud.

82

aw
Read these words aloud.

shawl   prawn   straw

crawl   drawer   spawn

thaw   dawn

◆ Finish these words.

cl_ _   dr_ _   j_ _

s_ _   fl_ _

◆ Read the words aloud.

◆ Look in a dictionary for the words you don't know.

◆ Can you find some new words for the **aw** phoneme box?

aw
1.
2.
3.
4.
5.

◆ Write a sentence for three of your words.

_____

_____

_____

Read your friend's new words aloud.

er

Write *er* to finish the words. Then join the words to the pictures.

farm _ _

jump _ _

hamm _ _

tig _ _

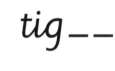

◆Read the words aloud.

◆Use the letters in the bubbles to make *er* words.

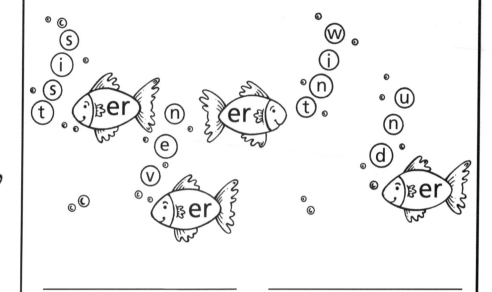

_____ _____

_____ _____

◆Read the words aloud.

Find three more *er* words. Write them.

84

er

Write *er* to finish the words. Then join the words to the pictures.

driv __ __

trous __ __ s

lett __ __

sing __ __

◆ Read the words aloud.

◆ Use the letters in the bubbles to make *er* words.

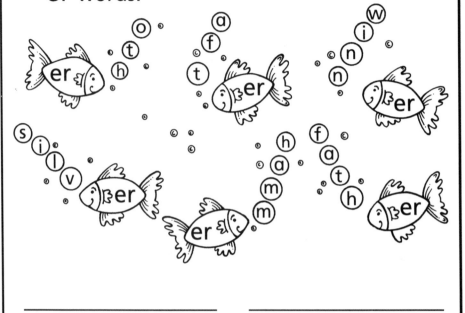

_____   _____

_____   _____

_____   _____

◆ Read the words aloud.

Find four more *er* words. Write them.

er

Write *er* to finish the words. Then join the words to the pictures.

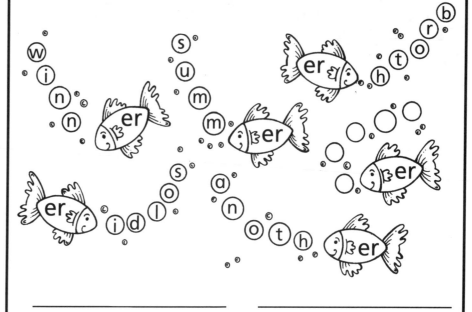

◆Use the letters in the bubbles to make *er* words. Find one of your own.

teach __ __

h __ __ d

m __ __ maid

dang __ __

◆Read the words aloud.

_____ _____

_____ _____

_____ _____

◆Read the words aloud.

Find five more *er* words. Write them.

ir

Do the *ir* crossword. Read the clues for the words going across and down.

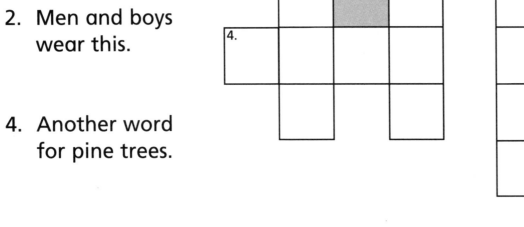

ACROSS

2. Men and boys wear this.

4. Another word for pine trees.

◆ Read the words aloud.

DOWN

1. This comes before 'second'.

2. You _____ your tea with a spoon.

3. This comes next after 'second'.

> See how many more *ir* words you can find.

86

ir

Do the *ir* crossword. Read the clues for the words going across and down.

DOWN

ACROSS

1. The person at the front of the line is _____.

3. The number after 29 is _____.

6. This flies in the sky and lays eggs.

2. You do this with a spoon in tea or coffee.

4. This comes after 'second'.

5. You wash your clothes when they're covered with _____.

◆ Read the words aloud.

See how many more *ir* words you can find.

ir

Do the *ir* crossword. Read the clues for the words going across and down.

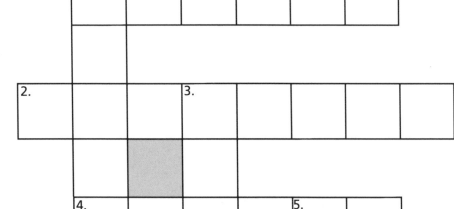

ACROSS

1. Elephants _____ water from their trunks.

2. You have candles on your _____ cake.

4. This comes after 29.

7. If you fall in mud, you get very ____.

DOWN

1. Ladies and girls wear this.

3. This is before 'fourth'.

5. When you need to sleep you are _____.

6. An evergreen tree.

◆ Read the words aloud.

See how many more *ir* words you can find.

88

ur

Use the letters in the balloons to make *ur* words.

_____

_____

_____

_____

◆ Look for the words in a dictionary.

◆ Read the words aloud.

Write sentences for two of the words.

90

ur

Use the letters in the balloons to make *ur* words.

_____

_____

_____

_____

_____

◆ Look for the words in a dictionary.

◆ Read the words aloud.

Write sentences for three of the words.

ur

Use the letters in the balloons to make *ur* words.

ch
ch

glar
b

ch
l

st
b

t
sp

n

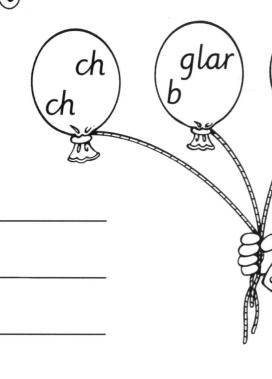

ur

_____

_____

_____

_____

_____

_____

◆ Look for the words in
a dictionary.

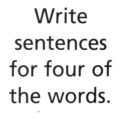

Write
sentences
for four of
the words.

◆ Read the words aloud.

91

ch

Sometimes the phoneme for *ch* sounds like *k*. Look for the words in the dictionary.

chemist

Christmas tree

choir

◆Choose the correct words to finish the sentences.

1. On 24 December we decorate our _____.

2. Mum bought my medicine at the _____.

3. I sing in the school _____.

Can you find more *ch* words with the phoneme *k*?

92

ch

Sometimes the phoneme for *ch* sounds like *k*. Look for the words in the dictionary.

◆ Choose the correct words to finish the sentences.

chaos

Christmas pudding

chord

chemist

1. We eat _____
   on 25 December.

2. Dad plays a _____ on his guitar.

3. We can buy medicine and cream at the _____ .

4. If everybody shouted out at once, it would be _____ .

Can you find more *ch* words with the phoneme *k*?

ch

Sometimes the phoneme for *ch* sounds like *k*. Look for the words in the dictionary.

christening

chasm

chrysalis

character

Christmas present

◆ Choose the correct words to finish the sentences.

1. A big hole in the ground is a _____.

2. Titch is my favourite _____.

3. My baby brother's _____ is tomorrow.

4. A caterpillar turns into a _____.

5. Granny gave me a really good _____ this year.

Can you find more *ch* words with the phoneme *k*?

Name _____   Date _____

↑ Fold ↓

95

ph

Look for these *ph* words in the dictionary.

photo

phoneme

phone

◆Read the words aloud.

◆Write a sentence for each word.

_____

_____

_____

_____

_____

_____

◆Ask your friend to read your sentences aloud.

photo phoneme phone

Name _____   Date _____

↑
Fold
↓

ph
Look for these **ph**
words in the dictionary.

◆ Write a sentence for each word.

phantom

phone

phoneme

photograph

_____

_____

_____

_____

_____

_____

_____

_____

◆ Ask your friend to read your
sentences aloud.

phantom phone phoneme photograph

96

Sheet 29c   Name _____   Date _____

Look
say
cover
write
check

Fold

97

ph
Look for these *ph* words in the dictionary.

physics

phrase

pharmacy

phonemes

photocopy

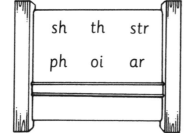

Pharmacy

| sh | th | str |
| ph | oi | ar |

◆Read the words aloud.

◆Write a sentence for each word.

_____

_____

_____

_____

_____

_____

_____

_____

_____

◆Ask your friend to read your sentences aloud.

wh
Write **wh** to finish the words. Then join the words to the pictures.

Sherft

__ __ale

__ __eel

__ __isper

◆Read the words aloud.

◆Choose the right **wh** word to finish the questions.

When   What   Why   Where

1. _____ are you going?

2. _____ do you want to eat?

3. _____ is the baby crying?

4. _____ are we going shopping?

Write two more sentences with **wh** words.

wh

Write **wh** to finish the words. Then join the words to the pictures.

_ _ eel

_ _ istle

_ _ iskers

_ _ ale

_ _ ite

◆ Read the words aloud.

◆ Choose the right **wh** word to finish the questions.

When What Why Where

1. _____ colour is your new coat?

2. _____ is your birthday?

3. _____ does a bird live?

4. _____ can't I go too?

5. _____ is Christmas day?

Write three more sentences with **wh** words.

100

wh

Write **wh** to finish the words. Then join the words to the pictures.

__ __isk

__ __eat

__ __isper

__ __ale

__ __istle

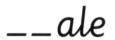

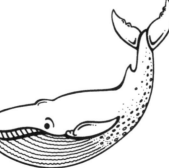

◆ Read the words aloud.

◆ Choose the right **wh** word to finish the questions.

When What Why Where

1. _____ is the train going to?

2. _____ is your favourite book?

3. _____ do you go to bed?

4. _____ do we have to breathe?

5. _____ sweets will you choose?

6. _____ is your mum's birthday?

Write four more sentences with **wh** words.

Compound words – 1

◆ Join together words from Box A and Box B to make a new word.

◆ Write the new word in Box C. One has already been done for you.

Box A	Box B	Box C
hand	side	1. *milkman*
~~milk~~	bag	2.
play	~~man~~	3.
in	time	4.

◆ The new words in Box C are called **compound words**.

Write two new compound words.

Compound words – 1

◆ Join together words from Box A and Box B to make a new word.

◆ Write the new word in Box C. One has already been done for you.

Box A	Box B	Box C
lamp	bin	1. *milkman*
week	ways	2.
~~milk~~	end	3.
side	post	4.
dust	~~man~~	5.

◆ The new words in Box C are called

compound words.

Write three new compound words.

Compound words – 1

◆ Join together words from Box A and Box B to make a new word.

◆ Write the new word in Box C. One has already been done for you.

Box A	Box B	Box C
play	~~man~~	1. milkman
cross	house	2.
some	side	3.
~~milk~~	times	4.
be	word	5.
light	ground	6.

◆ The new words in Box C are called **compound words**.

Write four new compound words.

Compound words – 2

◆ Draw a line through the compound words to make two smaller words.

◆ Write the words. One has been done for you.

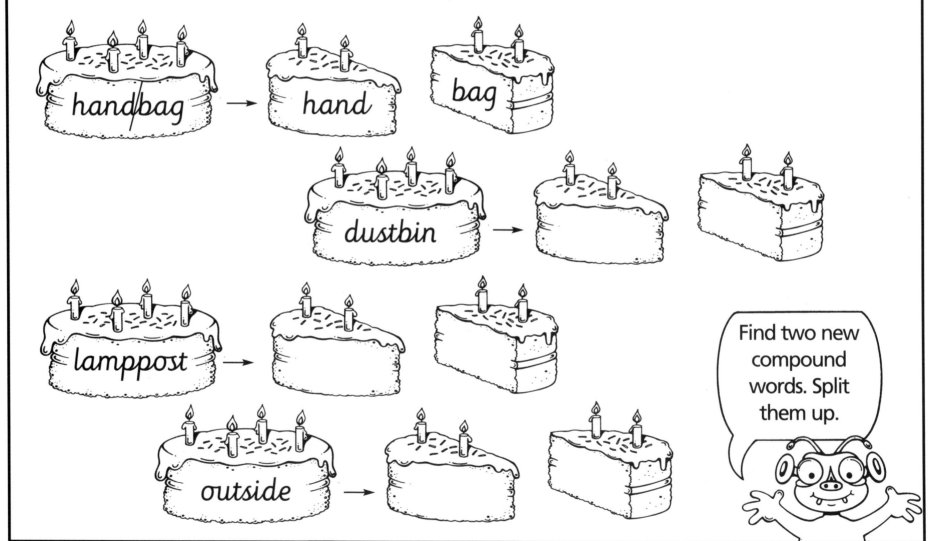

handbag → hand   bag

dustbin →

lamppost →

outside →

Find two new compound words. Split them up.

Compound words – 2

◆ Draw a line through the compound words to make two smaller words.

◆ Write the words. One has been done for you.

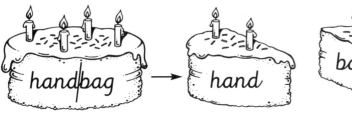 →

handbag → hand   bag

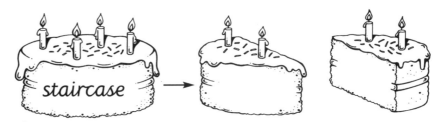

staircase →

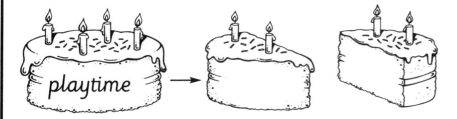

playtime →

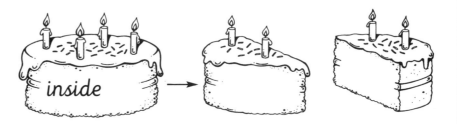

inside →

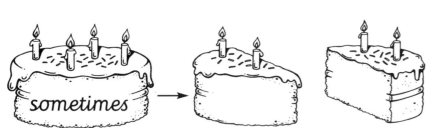

sometimes →

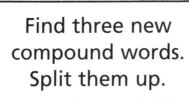

Find three new compound words. Split them up.

Compound words – 2

◆ Draw a line through the compound words to make two smaller words.

◆ Write the words. One has been done for you.

handbag → hand | bag

dustbin →

staircase →

blackbird →

weekend →

sideways →

inside →

Find four new compound words. Split them up.

Phonicability

SECTION 3

Revision of...

...vowel phonemes — ea, ear
...compound words
...wh, ph, ch

Revision – ea/ear, compound words, consonant digraphs

OVERALL AIMS

- ○ To sound, recognise and name the vowel phonemes 'ear' and 'ea'.
- ○ To name and write words that include these vowel phonemes.
- ○ To revise and consolidate compound words.
- ○ To revise and consolidate the consonant digraphs 'ch', 'ph' and 'wh'.

TEACHER'S NOTES

It is vital that children learn to listen to and sound the phonemes represented by digraphs, and vowel digraphs are no exception to this. The children must have the ability to hear a word in its different components if they are to develop good reading and spelling skills. Thus they need to be able to recognise the formation of vowel digraphs and the resulting phonemes, in order to sound a word successfully. This is especially so for a digraph that has the same spelling as, but a different phoneme from, another, as in the case of 'ear' and 'ea'.

Revision and consolidation of the rules learned earlier in the year are important. This is the final stage of formal phonics teaching and it is necessary to ensure that the children have assimilated and understood the work already covered.

Before distributing the activity sheets, read the instructions on each sheet to the groups.

LESSON ONE

Intended learning:

- ○ To listen to, name and sound the vowel phonemes 'ear' and 'ea'.
- ○ To name a word or object that contains these vowel phonemes.
- ○ To name, split and join compound words.
- ○ To listen to, name and sound the consonant digraphs 'ch', 'ph' and 'wh'.
- ○ To name a word or object that contains these consonant digraphs.

Starting point: whole class

Write the phoneme being taught/revised on the board and tell the children what phoneme it makes.

Play a game-in-the-round where the children take it in turns to say a word with that phoneme. The words may or may not rhyme – saying the correct phoneme is the important part.

Share an enlarged page from a magazine and circle each word containing the phoneme. Ask for volunteers to write the discovered words on the board.

Ask the children to write compound words on the board. Other children then split them into the smaller words. Repeat this vice versa.

Group activities

- ○ Ask the children to make a word tree of the phoneme being taught/revised. The trunk is labelled with the phoneme and the leaves all have a word written on them which contains that phoneme.
- ○ Use Generic sheet 3 to make a phoneme dice. The child has to give a word containing the phoneme on the dice face of their throw.
- ○ Make a collage of pictures of things containing the revised phoneme. Display the collage while the rule is being revised.
- ○ Ask the children to make a collection of objects/ pictures/models of things with the digraph in the names. Keep these on display while the digraph is being taught/revised.
- ○ Make word wheels to contain compound words split into their components.
- ○ Use Generic sheet 2 to make wordsearches of compound words.

Plenary session

Each group should report back on what they did. Use the phoneme tree to discuss the phoneme. Display it while the phoneme is being taught and consolidated. Do the same with the collection of objects/models/pictures.

Ask the children, "What was the phoneme you learned/revised today?", "What did you find difficult today?", "What did you find easy?" and "Did you find any new compound words?"

LESSON TWO

Intended learning:
- ○ To name and write words that include the vowel phonemes 'ear' and 'ea'.
- ○ To name and write words that include the consonant digraphs 'ch', 'ph' and 'wh'.
- ○ To name, write, split and join compound words.

Starting point: whole class

Write the previous lesson's phoneme on the board. Ask, "What phoneme is this?" and "What words have this phoneme in them?".

Ask for three or four volunteers to write words containing that phoneme on the board.

Play Hangman using words containing the new/revised phoneme. Ask for volunteers to be the Hangman.

Ask for some new compound words. Divide the board into three columns and put the compound word and its components into the three sections.

Introduce the activity sheets. Read the instructions on each sheet to the groups.

USING THE DIFFERENTIATED ACTIVITY SHEETS

Activity sheets a

These are for children who need repetition of the phoneme. They give practice in looking at, sounding and writing the phoneme being taught.

The sheet for compound words gives the opportunity for more practice in splitting the words.

Activity sheets b

These are for children who are able to do a little independent writing and who are capable of doing more work on a sheet. They give practice in looking at, sounding and writing the phoneme being taught. They encourage the writing of simple sentences incorporating the phoneme.

The sheet for compound words gives the opportunity for more practice in splitting the words.

Activity sheets c

These are for children who can confidently write a few words independently. They give practice in looking at, sounding and writing the phoneme being taught.

The sheet for compound words gives the opportunity for more practice in splitting the words.

Plenary session

Choose a child from each group to explain what their group did on their sheets. Ensure that across the term, every child has an opportunity to be their group's 'spokesperson'. Make a display of some of the sheets while that rule is still being taught/revised and consolidated.

Ask, "What have you learned from today's lesson?", "Was there anything you didn't understand about today's lesson?" and "What was the phoneme we learned/revised today?"

GENERIC SHEETS

- ○ Generic sheet 1 has blank phoneme boxes. These can be used to find new words with the required phoneme and record them. The sheets cane be used either as the basis of a search game or as a reference bank of words specifically containing that phoneme.
- ○ Generic sheet 2 has blank grids that can be used to design wordsearches or crosswords. Several of the activity sheets give this as a task and this generic sheet can be used as the photocopiable master. The grids are of differing sizes for different ability children.
- ○ Generic sheet 3 has the blank outline of a cube which can be copied onto card, cut out and used as a dice in phoneme games.
- ○ Generic sheet 4 has blanks which can be used for Pelmanism, dominoes or snap, as required. The appropriate phoneme can be written on each card.

110

ea
Read the poem.

Don't shake your head,

You don't have to dread

The phoneme **ea** as in **bread**.

You don't have to fret

Or get upset

'Cos it sounds just the same as in **bed**!

◆ What sound does **ea** make in the words in the poem?

◆ Make the **ea** word slide.

h
br
l
d

✂ ------------------

ead

✂ ------------------

Write a sentence for each word.

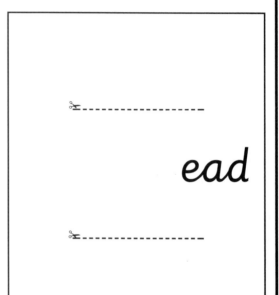

ea
Read the poem.

Don't shake your head,

You don't have to dread

The phoneme **ea** as in **bread**.

You don't have to fret

Or get upset

'Cos it sounds just the same as in **bed**!

◆ What sound does **ea** make in the words in the poem?

◆ Make the **ea** word slide.

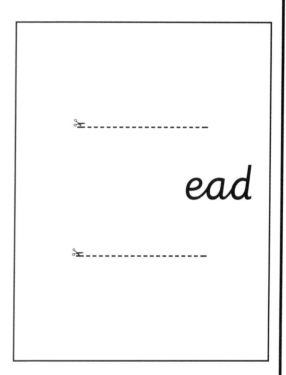

br

h

d

dr

thr

l

ead

✂ - - - - - - - - - - -

✂ - - - - - - - - - - -

Write a sentence for each word.

ea
Read the poem.

Don't shake your head,

You don't have to dread

The phoneme **ea** as in **bread**.

You don't have to fret

Or get upset

'Cos it sounds just the same as in **bed**!

◆ What sound does **ea** make in the words
in the poem?

◆ Make the **ea** word slide.

thr

inst

h

br

spr

d

l

dr

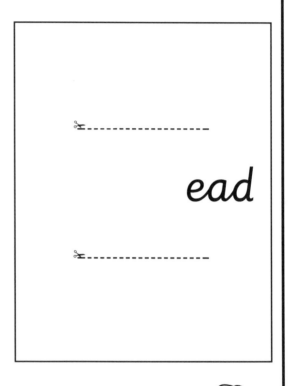

ead

Write a
sentence for
each word.

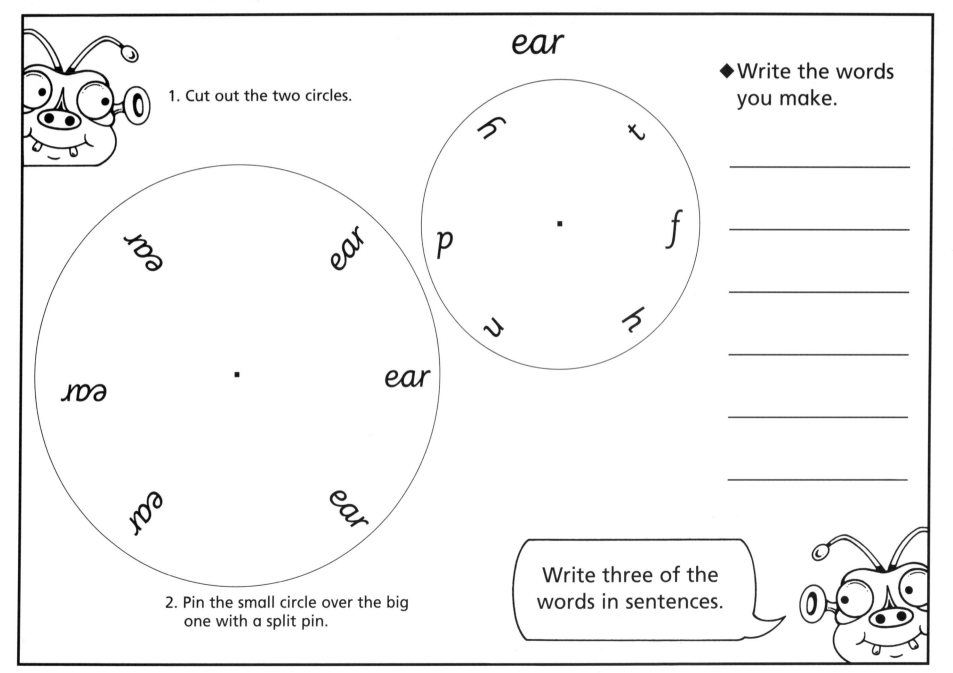

ear

1. Cut out the two circles.

2. Pin the small circle over the big one with a split pin.

◆ Write the words you make.

_____

_____

_____

_____

_____

_____

_____

Write three of the words in sentences.

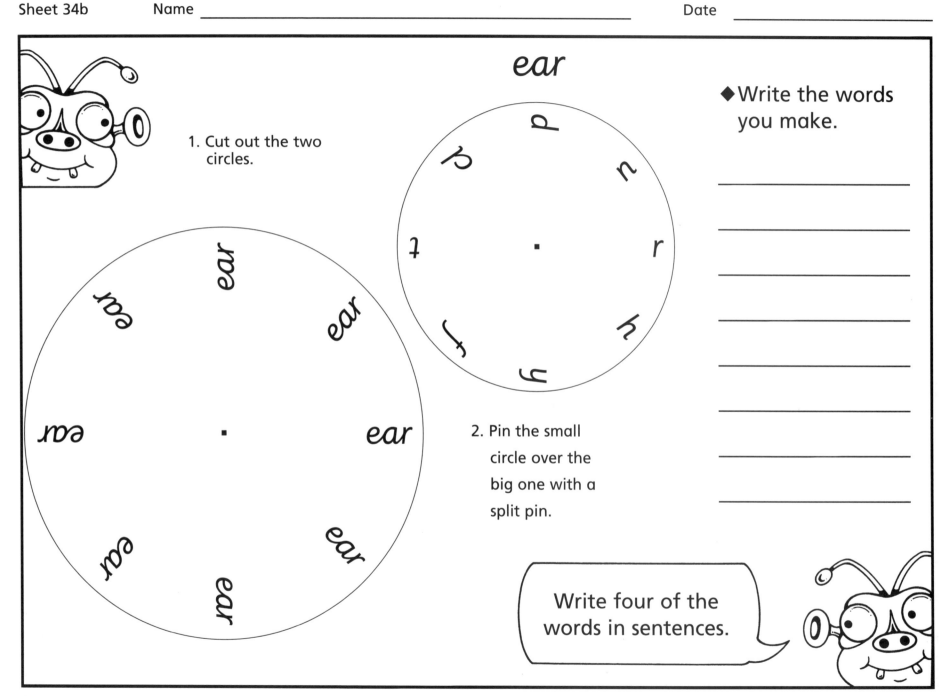

1. Cut out the two circles.

◆Write the words you make.

_____

_____

_____

_____

_____

_____

_____

_____

2. Pin the small circle over the big one with a split pin.

Write four of the words in sentences.

Name _____

Date _____

ear

1. Cut out the two circles.

◆ Write the words you make.

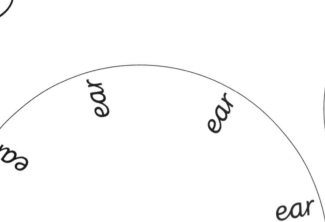

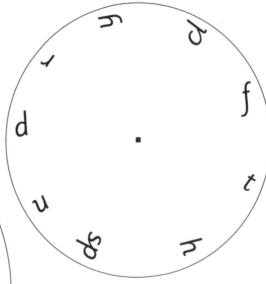

2. Pin the small circle
   over the big one
   with a split pin.

_____

_____

_____

_____

_____

_____

_____

_____

Write five of the
words in sentences.

116

Compound words

Split these compound words and write the two new smaller words.

bluebottle ⟶ ___ ___

jellyfish ⟶ ___ ___

earring ⟶ ___ ___

toenail ⟶ ___ ___

◆ Find the same words in the grid. You may go across or down. Some letters are used twice.

b	l	u	e	j	t
o	f	t	a	e	o
t	i	o	r	l	e
t	s	n	a	i	l
l	h	r	i	n	g
e	j	e	l	l	y

ear
ring
blue
bottle
jelly
fish
toe
nail

◆ Look for the compound words in the dictionary.

Make a new wordsearch with compound words.

Compound words

Split these compound words and write the two new smaller words.

football   → ___ ___

toothbrush   → ___ ___

kneecap   → ___ ___

greenhouse   → ___ ___

tonight   → ___ ___

◆ Find the same words in the grid. You may go across, up or down. Some letters are used twice.

r	f	g	r	e	e	n
t	o	o	t	h	n	i
k	o	h	b	s	t	g
n	t	o	a	u	o	h
e	p	u	l	r	f	t
e	a	s	l	b	h	o
p	c	e	s	f	t	g

tooth
brush
green
house
foot
ball
knee
cap
to
night

◆ Look for the compound words in the dictionary.

Make a new wordsearch with compound words.

Compound words

Split these compound words and write the two new smaller words.

understand   →   ____ ____

hairbrush   →   ____ ____

ribcage   →   ____ ____

lighthouse   →   ____ ____

without   →   ____ ____

eyeball   →   ____ ____

◆ Find the same words in the grid. You may go across or down and backwards or forwards. Some letters are used twice.

t	r	e	d	n	u	o	u
u	h	f	n	e	l	a	b
o	a	c	a	g	e	y	e
h	i	g	t	s	t	a	h
b	r	u	s	h	h	a	o
a	i	u	n	d	t	h	u
l	b	t	h	g	i	l	s
l	h	c	t	o	w	s	e

with
out
rib
cage
under
stand
eye
ball
light
house
hair
brush

◆ Look for the compound words in the dictionary.

Make a new wordsearch with compound words.

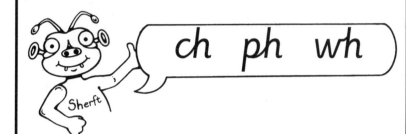

ch ph wh

Look for these words in the dictionary.

phonecard

chord

whale

Christmas

◆ Read the words aloud.

◆ Write a sentence for each word.

_____

_____

_____

_____

_____

_____

_____

_____

◆ Ask your friend to read your sentences aloud.

Look
say
cover
write
check

Fold ↑ ↓

119

phonecard chord whale Christmas

Name _____   Date _____

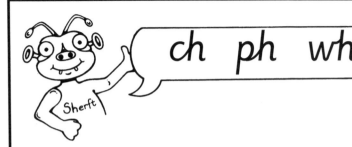

ch ph wh

Look for these words in the dictionary.

chrysalis

wheat

phonics

chrome

whimper

◆Read the words aloud.

◆Write a sentence for each word.

_____

_____

_____

_____

_____

_____

_____

_____

_____

_____

_____

◆Ask your friend to read your sentences aloud.

Look say cover write check

Fold

chrysalis wheat phonics chrome whimper

Name _____   Date _____

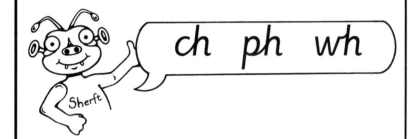

ch ph wh

Look for these words in the dictionary.

physical

whether

chlorine

phrase

white

chlorophyll

◆Read the words aloud.

◆Write a sentence for each word.

_____

_____

_____

_____

_____

_____

_____

_____

_____

_____

_____

◆Ask your friend to read your sentences aloud.

Look say cover write check

Fold

physical whether chlorine phrase white chlorophyll

121

Phonicability

SECTION 4

Generic Sheets

123

Generic Sheet 2

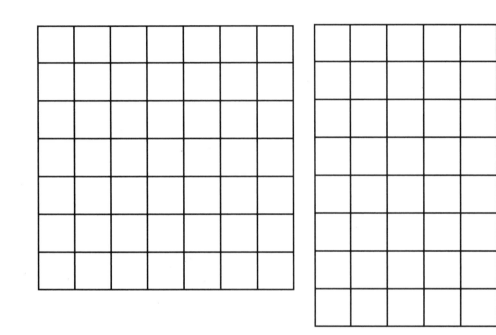

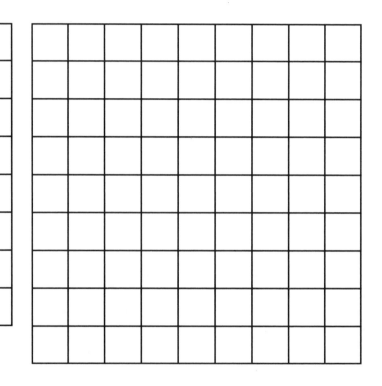

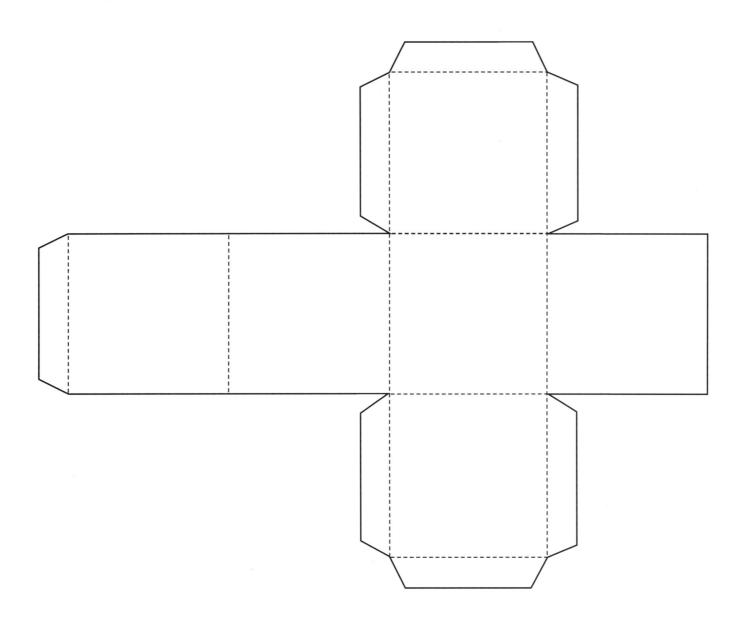

Generic Sheet 4

Phonics Record/Assessment Sheet

Name: _____

Year: _____ Level: _____ Date: _____

TARGET SKILL		NLSF REFERENCE
(Step 6)		
1 Knows the ten vowel phonemes: digraphs ai, ee, ie, oa, oo, or, ar, ir, oi, ou		Y2 Term 1: 1, 2, 3
2 Can segment to spell words containing vowel phonemes represented by more than one letter		Y1 Term 3: 1
3 Can blend to read words containing vowel phonemes represented by more than one letter		
		Y2 Term 1: 1, 2, 3, 4
(Step 7)		
1 Can segment to spell words containing vowel digraphs and trigraphs, ay, a-e, igh, y, i-e, o-e, oe, ew, ue, u-e, oy, ow, er, ur, aw, air, ear, oo		Y2 Term 2: 1, 2
2 Can blend to read words containing the same vowel digraphs and trigraphs		Y1 Term 3: 1, 3
Can recognise, split and rejoin compound words		

Comments: